X-MEN ANNUAL 2005
CⓍNTENTS

£6.99

IT CIRCLES THE GLOBE IN GEOSYNCHRONOUS ORBIT...

...A TECHNOLOGICAL MARVEL BRISTLING WITH ARMAMENTS THAT WOULD BE THE ENVY OF ANY ARMY ON EARTH.

ASTEROID M-- THE HOLLOWED-OUT SPACE ROCK THAT SERVES AS THE PRIMARY REFUGE FOR THE MUTANT MASTER OF MAGNETISM--

--MAGNETO--

--A BEING SO FEARED BY HUMANITY THAT SPECIAL PROTOCOLS HAVE BEEN PUT IN PLACE TO SAFE-GUARD AGAINST HIM.

БACK IN THE USSЯ
ARMAGEDDON IN RED

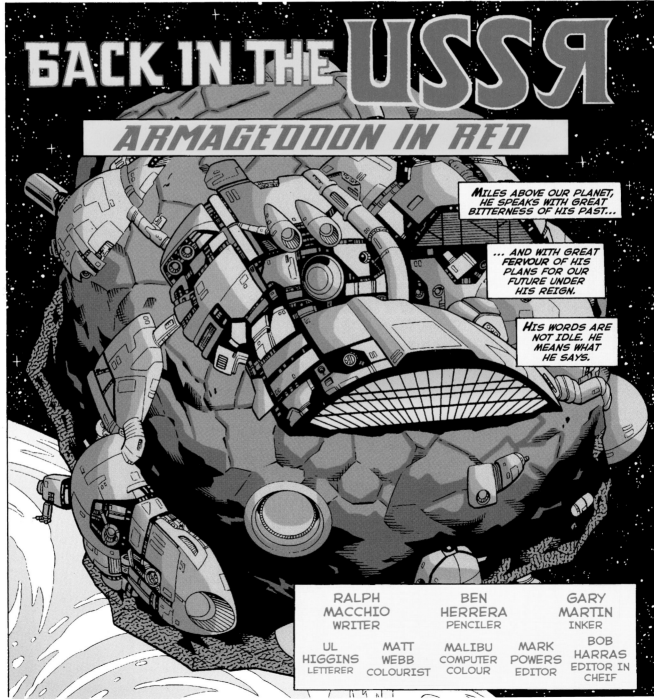

MILES ABOVE OUR PLANET, HE SPEAKS WITH GREAT BITTERNESS OF HIS PAST...

... AND WITH GREAT FERVOUR OF HIS PLANS FOR OUR FUTURE UNDER HIS REIGN.

HIS WORDS ARE NOT IDLE. HE MEANS WHAT HE SAYS.

RALPH MACCHIO WRITER		BEN HERRERA PENCILER		GARY MARTIN INKER
UL HIGGINS LETTERER	MATT WEBB COLOURIST	MALIBU COMPUTER COLOUR	MARK POWERS EDITOR	BOB HARRAS EDITOR IN CHEIF

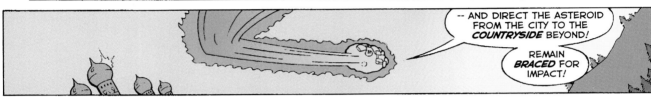

<ATTENTION! ON MY COMMAND-- YOU WILL ATTACK THOSE AT THE CRASH SITE!>*

* TRANSLATED FROM THE RUSSIAN -- ED-OVICH

WE HAVE REHEARSED SCENARIOS SUCH AS THIS AS WE PREPARED FOR THE HUMANS INEVITABLE ATTACKS ON US! THOUGH WE ARE NOT AT FULL STRENGTH--WE WILL TRIUMPH!

BUT RESTRAIN YOURSELVES UNTIL I GIVE THE COMMAND THERE MUST BE NO MARGIN FOR ERROR.

<FIRE!>

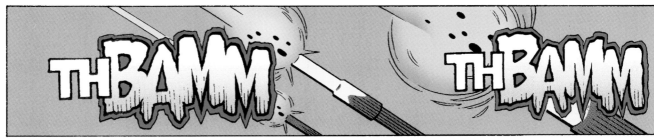

THBAMM   THBAMM

NOW, MY BROTHERHOOD-- FORWARD!

DON'T WATCH *THEM*, MASTER! LOOK AT THE FAITHFUL TOAD!

ONLY I HAVE THE ACROBATIC SKILLS TO DO--

--*THIS*!

BONK

YOU DO WELL, TOAD. CONTINUE.

WITH *PLEASURE*, MASTER!

NO BARRAGE OF SHELLS CAN PENETRATE MY MAGNETIC SCREEN!

EXHAUST YOUR ARSENAL--SEND AN *ENDLESS* AMOUNT OF ARMAMENTS--AND THE RESULTS WILL BE THE *SAME*!

THOOM

ptwang

BUT THE MASTER OF MAGNETISM DOES NOT EXCEL AT MERE *DEFENSE*--

--AS THE TWISTED TURRETS OF YOUR TANKS BESPEAK!

WRENNK

AND AS MAGNETO REVELS IN HIS DOMINANCE...

SVEEEESH

...THE MUTANT QUICKSILVER RUSHES TO AND FRO WITH SUCH BLINDING VELOCITY THAT A DEEP TRENCH IS DUG BEFORE THE ADVANCING TANKS.

MORE TANKS EMERGE FROM THE FOREST. THIS BATTLE COULD CONTINUE INDEFINITELY.

QUICKSILVER! SCARLET WITCH! TOAD! REJOIN ME! WE WILL SPEAK!

FURTHER CONFLICT IS MEANINGLESS WE HAVE SHOWN THEM OUR *STRENGTH*...

...NOW WE WILL *DEPART* BEFORE SUFFERING NEEDLESS INJURY.

DEPART? AN INTERESTING CHOICE OF WORDS, MAGNETO!

DON'T YOU MEAN *RETREAT?*

ONCE UPON A TIME YOU SAID WE WOULD *NEVER* HAVE TO RETREAT FROM OUR ENEMIES *AGAIN!*

THESE ARE MY ORDERS, PIETRO! WE ARE ON UNFAMILIAR SOIL-- FIGHTING AT LESS THAN FULL CAPACITY.

WOULD YOU SHED YOUR OWN SISTER'S BLOOD WHEN THERE IS SO LITTLE TO GAIN?

NO... I WOULD NOT.

DECADES AGO, I FLED INTO A FOREST WITH THE RUSSIAN ARMY AT MY BACK.

THEN THEY WERE THE LIBERATORS OF MY PRISON CAMP.

BUT THIS DAY MY DEBT TO THEM HAS BEEN FULLY ERASED.

SOON, THERE WILL BE A RECKONING...

CONTINUED ON PAGE 16

CYCLOPS

Real Name: Scott Summers
Height: 6'1"
Weight: 185 lbs
Eye Colour: Glowing red
Hair Colour: Brown

MUTANT POWERS:

Cyclops has the ability to emit powerful optic blasts from his eyes. He is forced to wear a ruby quartz visor at all times as he cannot control his mutant powers.

CASE HISTORY:

Scott Summers was raised in an orphanage, having lost both his parents at a young age. When his mutant abilities first manifested, Scott found himself pursued by an angry mob who were fearful of his destructive power. He was rescued by Professor X, who invited him to be the founding member of his new group of mutant superheroes, the X-Men.

Although he is a wise leader and a reliable friend, Scott is constantly hounded by the destructive nature of his mutation. Due to this he can be quite an introverted and rigid person. However, his wife and fellow team mate, Jean Grey, is always willing to help him overcome his doubts and fears.

SPEED	4
STRENGTH	5
INTELLIGENCE	5
FIGHTING SKILLS	8

PHOENIX

Real Name: Jean Grey
Height: 5'6"
Weight: 115 lbs
Eye Colour: Green
Hair Colour: Red

MUTANT POWERS:

Jean Grey has telepathic and telekinetic powers, allowing her to read people's minds and manipulate objects with her psyche.

CASE HISTORY:

As a child, Jean Grey's blossoming psychic powers caused her many problems. Her parents contacted Professor Charles Xavier who, realising Jean was a mutant, offered to help and train her. A few years later when Xavier created the X-Men he knew that Jean would be a valuable asset to the team and invited her to join.
As well as being an accomplished psychic, Jean can also tap into the mystical phoenix Force and use it to increase the potency of her powers ten-fold.

SPEED	3
STRENGTH	4
INTELLIGENCE	5
FIGHTING SKILLS	7

PROFESSOR X

Real Name: **Charles Xavier**
Height: **6'**
Weight: **190 lbs**
Eye Colour: **Blue**
Hair Colour: **Bald (blonde as a child)**

MUTANT POWERS:

Professor X has incredible mental powers which he can use to affect the minds of others. He can also access the spirit dimension known as the astral plane.

CASE HISTORY:

As a young boy Charles Xavier knew that his mutant powers were a great gift and could be used to help humanity. However he kept them a secret, cautious of what others would say. Many years later whilst working in Israel, he became friends with a young man named Erik Lehnsherr. Erik confided in Charles, telling him that he was also a mutant. The two were good friends but their opinions on mutant-kind were vastly different. Charles believed in peaceful co-operation between man and mutant, whereas Erik believed that mutants should rule over the less evolved humans. Their friendship eventually disintegrated and Charles returned to America to set up his school for gifted youngsters. Erik, pursuing his own agenda of mutant domination, became the super-villain known as Magneto.

Professor X's dream is the driving force behind the X-Men. He has sworn to protect a world that both fears and hates him, and will never give up hope that one day mutants and humans can live together in peace.

SPEED	4
STRENGTH	8
INTELLIGENCE	9
FIGHTING SKILLS	6

X-MEN

CONTINUED FROM PAGE 13

ELSEWHERE, THOUSANDS OF MILES DISTANT IN NEW YORK'S WESTCHESTER COUNTY, IS THE PRIVATE INSTITUTE CALLED THE XAVIER SCHOOL FOR GIFTED YOUNGSTERS...

...RUN BY CHARLES XAVIER, THE WORLD'S GREATEST TELE-PATH, THE INSTITUTE SECRETLY TRAINS MUTANTS TO DEAL WITH THE CHALLENGES OF A WORLD THAT FEARS THEIR EXISTENCE.

TODAY, THIS GROUP KNOWN AS THE X-MEN PRACTICES FOR COMBAT SITUATIONS IN THE DANGER ROOM...

...A CHAMBER CONSTRUCTED TO TEST EACH MUTANT'S SPECIFIC ABILITIES WITH SIMULATED PROGRAMS.

YIKES! LOST MY FOOTING.

I'LL STOP YOUR DESCENT TELEKINETI-CALLY, JUBILEE.

THANKS FOR THE SAVE, JEAN.

WELL, CYCLOPS? WE EARN OUR DAY'S KEEP, OR WHAT, HOMME?

WELL DONE, GAMBIT. YOU, STORM, WOL-VERINE AND JEAN PERFORMED TO CAPACITY DURING THE SEQUENCE.

AS FOR YOU, JUBILEE, THE EXERCISE WAS A FAILURE.

X-MEN. JOIN ME IMMEDIATELY IN THE WAR ROOM.

YES, SIR!

THAT SOUNDS URGENT! LET'S GET UPSTAIRS RIGHT AWAY!

MOMENTS LATER..

I AM PLEASED YOU HAVE COME QUICKLY, MY X-MEN. WE FACE A *SERIOUS* PROBLEM.

WHAT IS WRONG, PROFESSOR? I'VE NEVER SEEN YOU LOOK SO GRAVE.

I MAINTAIN *MANY* CONTACTS IN OUR GOVERNMENT--THOUGH TO THE WORLD AT LARGE, THIS SCHOOL IS A SIMPLE CENTRE FOR LEARNING.

I HAVE BEEN IN CONTACT WITH A HIGH-RANKING MILITARY OFFICIAL..

I AM PUTTING HIM ON THE SCREEN, LISTEN *CLOSELY* TO WHAT HE HAS TO SAY.

GREETIN'S, PEOPLE. WE GOT OURSELVES A *MESS* HERE. SEEMS THE HOME BASE O' YER OLD SPARRING PARTNER, MAGNETO...

...*ASTEROID M*, WAS SENT CRASHIN' TO THE GROUNDS IN SOME WOODS OUTSIDE O' MOSCOW.

DON'T KNOW *HOW* THIS COULD O' HAPPENED. WE KEEP ASTEROID M UNDER TWENTY-FOUR HOUR *SURVEILLANCE*, AS YOU DO.

WE GOT TWO THINGS FIGURED. ONE, THE WRECKAGE LANDED SOMEWHERE CLOSE TO THE *SOVIET MISSILE BASE*, AND TWO...

...IF MAGNETO REACHES THAT BASE 'FORE ANYONE ELSE DOES, THERE'S NO TELLIN' *WHAT* HE'LL DO. HE'S GOTTA THINK ASTEROID M WAS ATTACKED--

--WHEN THE TRUTH IS, THE WORLD'S SO *SCARED* O' MAGNETO THAT EVERY NATION KEEPS ITS DISTANCE. NOW, I'M TECHNICALLY COMMITTING *TREASON* BY DOIN' THIS--

--BUT I'M ASKIN' YOU TO SEND YER TEAM O' MUTANTS IN TO PREVENT MAGNETO FROM GAININ' CONTROL O' THEM SILOS. I THINK YER BOYS ARE THE *ONLY* CHANCE WE GOT.

SOVIET TROOPS ENGAGED HIM, ACCORDIN' TO OUR INTELLIGENCE. AND OUR *LATEST* ESTIMATE IS THAT WE'VE GOT *TWO HOURS* BEFORE THE WORLD IS AT THE *MERCY* O' THAT MADMAN.

I'M DUE TO BRIEF THE PRESIDENT, SO WE AIN'T GONNA BE SPEAKIN' FOR A WHILE. JUST MAKE SURE YA DO THE JOB -- *PRONTO!*

NICK FURY OUT.

ELSEWHERE, IN A FOREST MILES OUTSIDE OF MOSCOW, MAGNETO AND HIS PARTY COME UPON A CLEARING...

WE SEEM TO HAVE LOST OUR PURSUERS, AND -- WHAT IS THIS?

A *NUCLEAR WEAPONS* FACILITY. ONE OF *MANY* WHICH DOTS THIS ENORMOUS COUNTRY, CONTAINING THE ELEMENTS OF *DOOMSDAY.*

I BELIEVE WE MAY MAKE... *USE* OF THIS PLACE.

TOAD! QUICKSILVER! ENTER THE COMPOUND AND DISARM THE GUARDS!

AS YOU *WISH*, MASTER. *WATCH* HOW MANY THE TOAD TAKES OUT -- *MORE* THAN QUICKSILVER WILL!

FWOOM!

TOO LATE! TOO LATE!

I WILL BE ON YOU BEFORE YOUR WEAPONS RAISE!

WHAT IS THIS BLUR THAT -- *AAK!*

WELL DONE! WE MAY NOW ENTER IN A MANNER BEFITTING THE MASTER OF MAGNETISM AND THOSE WHO SERVE HIM.

WRONK

I WILL NOT FAIL YOU, MAGNETO. I WILL CAST A HEX THAT DRASTICALLY **INCREASES** THE CHANCES OF THE CONCRETE CRUMBLING...!

IF WE ARE TO ENTER THE BUILDING, WE MUST FIRST MAKE OUR WAY THROUGH THIS HUGE, CONCRETE DOOR.

CONCRETE IS NOT METAL -- SO MY OWN POWERS WILL **NOT** SUFFICE.

SCARLET WITCH... THIS IS WHERE **YOU** MAY TRULY PROVE THE EFFICIANCY OF YOUR PROBABILITY ALTERING PROWESS.

MOMENTS PASS WITH NO REACTION.

I MUST **CONTINUE** TO CAST MY HEX. I MUST **PROVE** MYSELF WORTHY OF THIS MAN WHO HAS TAKEN US ALL UNDER HIS WING

WILL REDOUBLE MY EFFORTS -- MORE -- **MORE** -- THE PROBABILITIES MUST ALIGN WITH **MY** DESIRE... MAKE THEM A **REALITY!**

YES -- SMALL CRACKS APPEARING -- GROWING **LARGER!** MUST CONTINUE -- MAKE IT **REAL** -- MAKE IT **HAPPEN!**

SKRMM

IS THERE NO *END* TO THIS NUISANCE? DEAL WITH THEM!

SEE, MASTER! ONCE *AGAIN* THE TOAD IS *FIRST* TO DO YOUR BIDDING! NONE OF THE OTHERS SERVE YOU AS *WELL* AS *I* DO! SEE!

TOAD -- SHUT UP!

WHOK

THUMP

I WILL OPEN THIS ELEVATOR DOOR WHICH WILL GIVE US ACCESS TO THE GUTS OF THE OPERATION BELOW.

EH? A FORCE BEAM STRIKING THE DOOR?

ZEKK

HOLD IT RIGHT *THERE!* THAT ELEVATOR'S OUT OF SERVICE -- AS OF *NOW!*

MASTER?

YOU'VE BEEN GIVIN' DE MUTANTS A *BAD* NAME, HOMME. WE GONNA PUT A *STOP* TO IT NOW.

AIN'T *DAT* ON DE MARK, SUMMERS?

YOU GOT THAT RIGHT, GAMBIT!

YOU'VE BEEN *SOLO* WHEN WE'VE TANGLED IN THE PAST, MAGNETO. FEELING LIKE YOU NEED A LITTLE *HELP* LATELY? FEELING *OLD?*

CRUSH THEM! TEACH THESE STOOGES OF XAVIER THE *ERROR* OF THEIR WAYS!

QUIT THE *CHATTERIN'*, CYKE! I'M READY TO *SLICE AN' DICE!*

WE'VE *HEARD* ABOUT YOU, *X-MEN!* AND WHEN WE GET *DONE* WITH YOU -- YOU'LL BE *COWERING* UNDER THE *COVERS* AT THE MENTION OF OUR NAMES!

SAVE SOME FOR THE *TOAD*, QUICKSILVER! *I* WANT THEM, TOO!

ATTACK WITH *CAUTION!* THEY WON'T FALL *EASILY!* XAVIER *DOES* TRAIN HIS CHARGES!

WILL YOU BE AT OUR SIDE, MAGNETO?

NO.

I WILL BE *BELOW.*

CONTINUED ON PAGE 28

23

THE BEAST'S BAMBOOZLING BRAIN-TEASERS!

Salutations! My name is Dr Henry McCoy, though you ma[y] know me better by my X-Men *nom de plume*, The Beast.

As the resident X-Men intellectual, I have prepared for you a selecti[on] of intricate enigmas designed to boost your brainpower and invigorate your minds!

X-MEN ROLL CALL!

Twelve of my most trusted mutant comrade's names are hidden in the word grid below.
Can you find them all?

W	K	E	G	A	M	B	I	T	J	A	F
Q	I	S	P	E	M	B	V	Z	W	N	U
X	C	Y	C	L	O	P	S	O	J	G	I
R	Q	X	M	R	B	W	L	U	E	E	C
O	O	E	D	T	M	V	B	T	A	L	E
S	L	G	K	J	E	I	V	T	N	A	M
S	K	E	U	R	L	B	I	L	G	V	A
E	N	E	I	E	L	S	M	E	R	N	N
F	K	N	E	Y	M	B	R	F	E	J	F
O	E	D	A	R	H	X	O	T	Y	A	I
R	E	L	W	A	R	C	T	H	G	I	N
P	G	E	C	O	L	O	S	S	U	S	F

- ⊗ CYCLOPS
- ⊗ JUBILEE
- ⊗ STORM
- ⊗ ANGEL
- ⊗ COLOSSUS
- ⊗ GAMBIT
- ⊗ ICE MAN
- ⊗ PROFESSOR X
- ⊗ JEAN GREY
- ⊗ ROGUE
- ⊗ NIGHTCRAWLER
- ⊗ WOLVERINE

DEADLY DISGUISE!

Shape-shifting mutant terrorist, **Mystique**, has managed to infiltrate the X-Mansion by assuming the form of Nightcrawler. Help the X-Men identify her by spotting the six differences between these two pictures.

POWER PLAY!

Test your mutant insight by matching up each of these X-Men to their appropriate powers.

PROFESSOR X

CYCLOPS

WEATHER MANIPULATION

OPTICAL LASER

ENHANCED HEALING FACTOR

TELEPATHY

WOLVERINE

STORM

INTRUDER ALERT!

The security systems have detected intruders in the grounds of the Xavier Mansion! Can you recognise these mutants caught on camera?

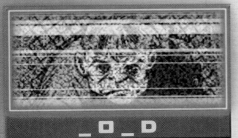

_ O _ D

_ _ G _ E _ _

S _ _ R _ E _ W _ _ _ H

_ _ I _ K _ _ L _ _ _

INSIDE THE X-MANSION!

To most members of the public, Xavier's school for gifted youngsters is nothing more than a specialist institute dealing with highly intelligent children. They are unaware that its real purpose is to train and educate young mutants in the use of their special abilities. Even more of a secret is the fact that it is also the base of the mutant super-hero team, **The X-Men.**

✕ REAL SCHOOL

Although the School teaches young mutants how to use their powers, they still have to study more traditional classes as well.

✕ COMMUNICATIONS GRID

The communications array is hidden within the roof of the X-Mansion. It is so powerful that it can contact the X-Men wherever they are on the planet.

GROUND LEVEL

✕ RECONSTRUCTION

Over the years the Xavier institute has been destroyed and rebuilt many times. During its most recent rebuilding a large amount of highly advanced Shi'ar technology was incorporated into the mansion. One of these alien upgrades is a team of robotic 'caretakers' who are responsible for the upkeep of the building and its equipment.

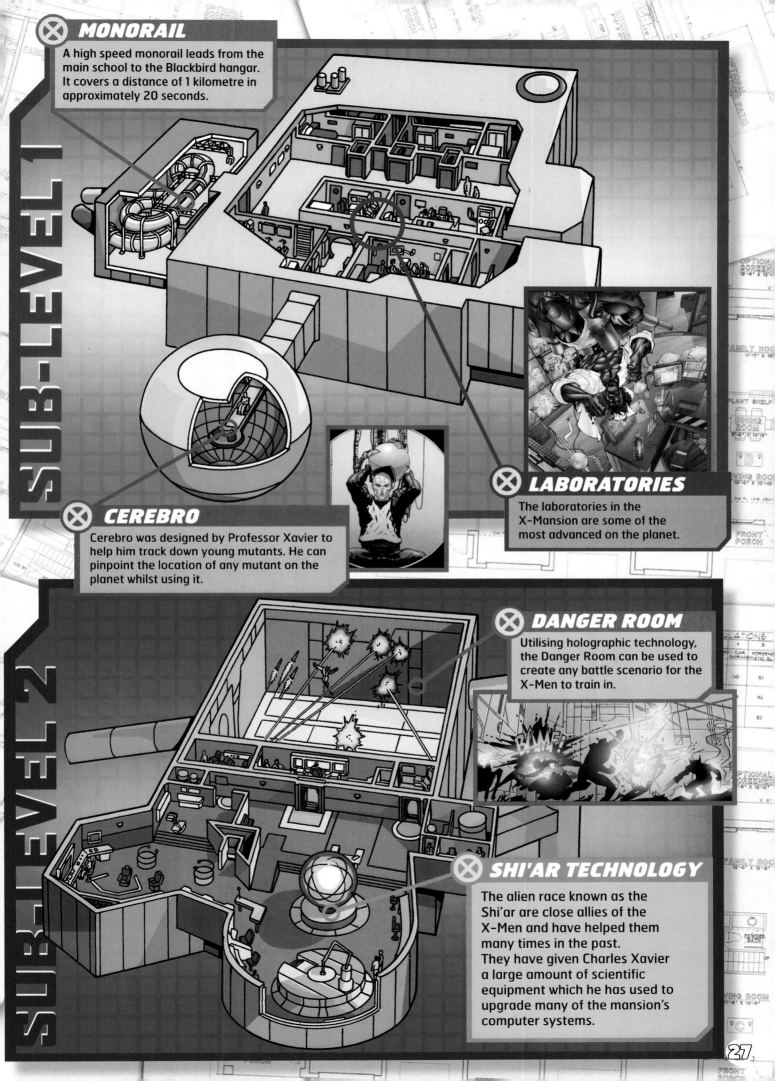

⊗ MONORAIL

A high speed monorail leads from the main school to the Blackbird hangar. It covers a distance of 1 kilometre in approximately 20 seconds.

⊗ CEREBRO

Cerebro was designed by Professor Xavier to help him track down young mutants. He can pinpoint the location of any mutant on the planet whilst using it.

⊗ LABORATORIES

The laboratories in the X-Mansion are some of the most advanced on the planet.

⊗ DANGER ROOM

Utilising holographic technology, the Danger Room can be used to create any battle scenario for the X-Men to train in.

⊗ SHI'AR TECHNOLOGY

The alien race known as the Shi'ar are close allies of the X-Men and have helped them many times in the past.
They have given Charles Xavier a large amount of scientific equipment which he has used to upgrade many of the mansion's computer systems.

CONTINUED FROM PAGE 23

SCOTT -- WHAT'S HAPPENING TO THE CEILING? THERE ARE *CRACKS* APPEARING?

MY SISTER -- WHAT?

I AM USING MY HEX POWER TO *CAUSE* IT TO CRACK, PIETRO.

THE ONE LEAPING TOWARD US -- I'LL TELEKINETICALLY SLAM HIM INTO THE WALL!

THAMP

OOOMPH!

TOAD!

THE WHITE-HAIRED ONE -- SHE GESTURES AND I FEEL MYSELF *SLOWING.*

YOU WILL APPROACH NO FURTHER, FLEET FOOTED ONE!

GUST OF *WIND* -- BRINGING ME TO A *HALT!*

ZZEKK

EXCELLENT SET-UP, STORM. YOU'VE MOVED HIM INTO POSITION --

-- NOW, I'LL TAKE HIM DOWN!

LUCKILY, WE DUCKED OUT OF THE WAY IN TIME.

DE FEMME IS *MINE*, CYCLOPS. GONNA TAKE HER DOWN WIT' KINETICAL-LY-CHARGED CARDS!

MY BROTHER AND THE TOAD -- TAKEN OUT SO *SKILLFULLY*!

NO TIME TO CAST A HEX BEFORE HE THROWS THOSE GLOW-ING CARDS!

AIIIIEEE*!!*

TZZZTTTRAKK

AND BELOW, NEARING THE COMMAND CENTRE...

THERE WAS ONLY A SCATTERED RESISTANCE TO MY PRESENCE. NOW I AM IN SIGHT OF THE MISSILE CONTROL ROOM.

WAIT -- A SEVERAL FOOT THICK STEEL DOOR HAS DROPPED INTO PLACE!

I WILL *NOT* BE DENIED!

THE NERVE CENTRE WILL BE *MINE!*

SPROOM

SHRAKK

He's put up a *magnetic wall* between us!

My power is *ineffective* as well.. but we *must* find a way through!

Can't cut through even with my *adamantium claws!*

Let's see how long de barrier lasts when it's *kinetically charged!*

You will do *nothing* until you contend again with us!

Wait -- please! Listen to me!

Magneto *isn't* just assuming control of this base for merely *blackmail* purposes!

He actually plans to *launch* nuclear missiles! Do you hear me? *He's going to launch!!*

Surely not even *Magneto* would attempt so *monumental* a folly!

O-of course not, my brother. And even if he *did* -- there are *safeguards* that would prevent one man from succeeding.

Master?

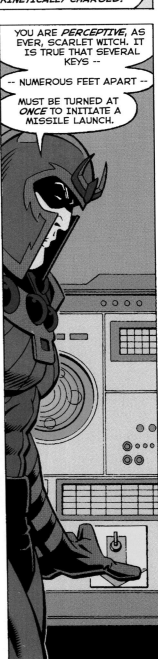

You are *perceptive,* as ever, Scarlet Witch. It is true that several keys --

-- numerous feet apart --

-- must be turned at *once* to initiate a missile launch.

31

WHEN ONE CAN HARNESS THE SUPREME POWER OF MAGNETISM TO TURN THOSE KEYS AT THE *SAME* MOMENT --

KLIK

KLIK

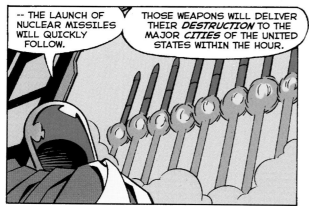

-- THE LAUNCH OF NUCLEAR MISSILES WILL QUICKLY FOLLOW.

THOSE WEAPONS WILL DELIVER THEIR *DESTRUCTION* TO THE MAJOR *CITIES* OF THE UNITED STATES WITHIN THE HOUR.

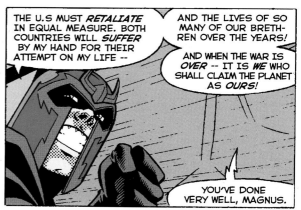

THE U.S MUST *RETALIATE* IN EQUAL MEASURE. BOTH COUNTRIES WILL *SUFFER* BY MY HAND FOR THEIR ATTEMPT ON MY LIFE --

AND THE LIVES OF SO MANY OF OUR BRETH-REN OVER THE YEARS!

AND WHEN THE WAR IS *OVER* -- IT IS *WE* WHO SHALL CLAIM THE PLANET AS *OURS*!

YOU'VE DONE VERY WELL, MAGNUS.

ON THE SCREEN WHO -- ?!

YOU PRATTLE ON LIKE A *BUFFOON*, MAGNETO. IT WAS *NEITHER* THE RUSSIANS NOR THE WEST WHICH SHOT DOWN ASTEROID M.

IT WAS *I*. AND ALL THAT YOU HAVE DONE SINCE ITS CRASH IS SO *PREDICTABLE*. YOUR ANGER -- YOUR PETULANCE -- YOUR *ARROGANCE*...

... ALL WORKED TO *PERFECTION* WITHIN MY SCHEME, FROM THE START YOU HAVE DONE *ONLY* WHAT I WANTED -- *ONLY* WHAT I *FORESAW*.

IN TRUTH, *THE ARCHITECT* OF TODAY'S DRAMA IS THE VERY BRINGER OF GENETIC HOLOCAUST --

--APOCALYPSE!

CONTINUED ON PAGE 36

32

THE BLACKBIRD

The X-Men's jet is an experimental long range aircraft, acquired by Professor Xavier from the global police force S.H.I.E.L.D. Although it is based on the Lockheed Blackbird, the design has been radically altered, incorporating both alien Shi'ar technology and improvements created by part-time X-Men team mate, Forge.

BLACKBIRD DATA:

- **WING SPAN:** 62 feet 6 inches
- **LENGTH:** 88 Feet 4 inches
- **HEIGHT:** 19 feet 2 inches
- **MAX. SPEED:** 3500 mph
- **RANGE:** 12,600 miles
- **MAX. CREW:** 7
- **OTHER:** Possesses stealth capabilities and limited space travel (the craft cannot leave Earth's orbit).

Afterburner

Wing Flaps

Communications Array

Ejector Seat Hatch

Pilot Seat / Co-Pilot Seat

Vertical Thruster Cluster

The Blackbird is a VTOL (Vertical Take-Off and Landing) craft.

Main Engine

ECM (Electronic Counter Measure) Controls

The X-Jet has a direct link to the main Cerebro unit at Xavier's Mansion. Using this, the X-Men can pinpoint and track the location of a mutant whilst in flight.

Radar Assembly

X-DATA COMM

GAMBIT

Real Name: **Remy LeBeau**
Height: **6'1"**
Weight: **175 lbs**
Eye Colour: **Red**
Hair Colour: **Brown**

SPEED	4
STRENGTH	4
INTELLIGENCE	4
FIGHTING SKILLS	7

MUTANT POWERS:

Gambit has the ability to tap into the potential energy stored inside an object, causing it to explode. His weapon of choice is usually a playing card, which he charges with power and then flings at his opponents.

CASE HISTORY:

Raised on the mean streets of New Orleans, Gambit was forced to resort to stealing to survive. By the time he was an adult he had become an expert thief and street-hustler. Due to a disagreement between two underworld organisations known as The Thieves Guild and The Assassins Guild, Gambit was forced to flee the city.

He was nominated for X-Men membership after he met Storm and helped her defeat a powerful mutant called The Shadow King. Although Gambit is very secretive about his dark past, he is sworn to Professor X's cause and would never let a fellow team mate down.

STORM

Real Name: **Ororo Munroe**
Height: **5'11"**
Weight: **127 lbs**
Eye Colour: **Blue**
Hair Colour: **White**

MUTANT POWERS:

Storm's mutation allows her to have complete control over the weather. This gives her a multitude of abilities from summoning winds to carry her through the air, to hurling lightning bolts at opponents.

SPEED	6
STRENGTH	4
INTELLIGENCE	4
FIGHTING SKILLS	7

CASE HISTORY:

Storm spent most of her childhood in her mother's ancestral home of Kenya. Using her mutant powers to help the African tribes-people, she could bring rains to stop the droughts and perform other such seemingly miraculous feats.
When the living island, Krakoa, captured the original X-Men, Charles Xavier found Storm and asked if she would join his new team. Since that day, Storm has become a valued member of the group and an expert warrior in battle.

DATA FILES

WOLVERINE

Real Name: **James Howlett (birth name), currently known as Logan**
Height: **5'3"**
Weight: **195 lbs**
Eye Colour: **Brown**
Hair Colour: **Black**

MUTANT POWERS:

Wolverine's body is laced with the indestructible metal, adamantium, plus he has an accelerated healing factor, making him incredibly resilient to damage. He also has a set of razor sharp claws on each hand.

CASE HISTORY:

Logan's past is a mystery. All that is known for sure is that at some point in his life he was involved in a horrific military experiment codenamed Weapon X. During this experiment his body was laced with an indestructible metal called adamantium and his memory was erased. Wolverine managed to escape from the Weapon X facility and was left in an insane bestial state. A couple called James and Heather Hudson, who worked for the Canadian government, found him.

They nursed Wolverine back to health and intended for him to join the new Canadian super-hero team, Alpha Flight. However, he was also approached by Professor Xavier to join the X-Men. Due to his guilt over his secret love for Heather, Wolverine agreed to join Charles Xavier's team.

Wolverine is an exceptional fighter but, due to his feral nature, has the tendency to go into a berserk rage when he is under extreme pressure in combat. The X-Men know to treat him with extreme caution when this happens, as he will lash out at the nearest target whether they are friend or foe.

SPEED	4
STRENGTH	5
INTELLIGENCE	5
FIGHTING SKILLS	9

X-MEN

YOU HAVE DONE MY WILL *SUPERB-LY!* NUCLEAR ARMAGEDDON WILL SOON BE VISITED UPON THE *WORLD!*

AND THROUGH THE *CHAOS* I HAVE LONG SOUGHT TO FORMENT, THE STRONG WILL BE CULLED FROM THE WEAK!

FOR ONLY THESE ARE FIT TO *SURVIVE.*

NO! I HAVE HEARD ENOUGH!

MAGNETO IS NO MAN'S LACKEY!

SKRASH

THE BARRIER HE IMPRISONED US BEHIND -- HE IS DISSOLVING IT!

THERE IS NO FURTHER NEED OF THIS.

NOW WE MAY *STRIKE BACK* AT THIS MAN WHOSE ACTIONS WILL BRING *DEATH* TO MILLIONS.

YOU'D BETTER TURN AROUND, BIG MAN! AT LEAST HAVE THE *GUTS* TO LOOK US IN THE EYE AS WE TAKE YOU *APART!*

YEAH! WE'RE REALLY SORRY YOU WERE PLAYIN' THE BIG A'S TUNE WITHOUT KNOWIN' IT --

-- BUT LIFE'S FULL O' LITTLE DISAPOINTMENTS, BUB!

STAY *BACK*, WANDA. I WILL NOT ACT OUT OF ANGER -- THAT WOULD PLAY INTO HIS HANDS AGAIN.

I WILL SIMPLY SHOW APOCALYPSE A DEMONSTRATION OF NAKED...

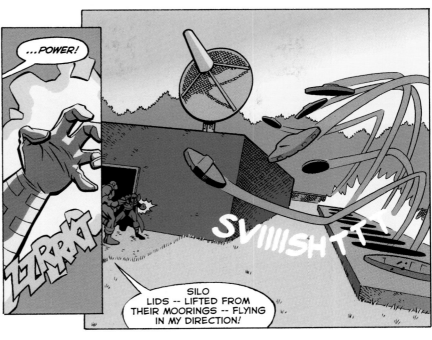

...POWER!

ZZRRRT

SVIIIISHTTT

SILO LIDS -- LIFTED FROM THEIR MOORINGS -- FLYING IN MY DIRECTION!

BAH! WHAT A *PATHETIC* DISPLAY! IT IS LITTLE MORE THAN AN ANNOYANCE TO ONE SUCH AS I!

BA TWAMM

THEN IT HAS SERVED ITS PURPOSE.

DO NOT *TOY* WITH ME, MUTANT!

TURNABOUT HAS ITS SMALL PLEASURES.

REMEMBER MY WORDS AS YOUR WORLD CRUMBLES AROUND YOU.

YOU WILL LEARN WHAT IT MEANS TO TREAT MAGNETO WITH IMPUNITY!

THE HOLLOW WORDS OF A HOLLOW MAN... MEANINGLESS AND IMPOTENT.

AND BELOW, IN THE BASE'S OPERATION ROOM...

NO WAY WE GONNA MAKE IT TO THE BLACKBIRD TO CONTACT XAVIER, JEAN. NOT WIT' APOCALYPSE DERE MAKIN' *TROUBLE.*

GOTTA COBBLE DIS COMMUNICATION STUFF TOGETHER! ONLY XAVIER CAN LET DE BRASS KNOW DAT MAGNETO'S GONNA *STOP* DE MISSILES 'FORE DEY EXPLODE.

I KNOW, GAMBIT. BUT I CAN'T SEEM TO GET THROUGH TELEPATHI- CALLY TO THE PROFESSOR.

IT MUST BE THE GREAT DISTANCE BETWEEN HERE AND THE STATES. BUT I'LL KEEP TRYING, I MUST...

DON'T STRAIN YOURSELF, *GAL.* JUST MADE DE FINAL CONNECTIONS. T'INK WE GOT IT NOW.

CONTINUED ON PAGE 44

41

ON THE HUNT!

LISTEN UP, BUB! I've been hunting that dog, Sabretooth, all day and I need your help.

He's hiding in an abandoned military complex, but the dirty rat has activated the base's security systems. Help me get past each of the traps so we can take the fur-ball down!

PUZZLE 1 — SHORT CIRCUIT

Sabretooth has managed to lockdown the outer security doors.

I need you to short out the system by finding which button on the circuit board doesn't have a red one next to it!

RESTRICTED
AUTHORISED PERSONNEL ONLY

THANKS, KID! THOSE DOORS WERE SO THICK THAT EVEN MY ADAMANTIUM CLAWS WEREN'T GONNA DO SPIT TO 'EM!

A B C D E F G
1 2 3 4 5 6 7 8 9 10

ANSWER:

PUZZLE 2 — BREAK IN

It looks like big, dumb and ugly has activated some of the guard robots so I'm gonna have to watch my step.

Can you work out which path to take so we can get through safely?

FINISH

ANSWER:

1 →
2 →
3 →

START

3 NUMBER CRUNCHIN'

The next room is guarded by a mutant-detecting laser sentry grid, so you're gonna have to deactivate the system by yourself.

In each grid work out what the two horizontal columns of numbers add up to, then work out what number needs to go in the middle so the vertical column adds up to the same number.

I'm countin' on you, kid - don't let me down!

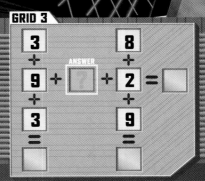

GRID 1

$$1 + 5 + 2$$
$$+ \text{ANSWER } \boxed{?} +$$
$$6 + 1 + 1$$
$$= \boxed{\ }$$
$$\boxed{\ } \quad \boxed{\ }$$

GRID 2

$$3 + 4 + 1$$
$$+ \text{ANSWER } \boxed{?} +$$
$$3 + 3 + 2$$
$$= \boxed{\ }$$
$$\boxed{\ } \quad \boxed{\ }$$

GRID 3

$$3 + 9 + 3$$
$$+ \text{ANSWER } \boxed{?} +$$
$$8 + 2 + 9$$
$$= \boxed{\ }$$
$$\boxed{\ } \quad \boxed{\ }$$

PASSCODE: ☐ ☐ ☐

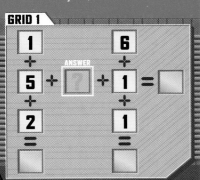

> MY NOSE IS TELLING ME THAT FLEA-BAG AIN'T FAR AWAY NOW! LET'S MOVE, SOLDIER!

I've cornered him in a wing of the compound and he's gotta be hiding behind one of these doors.

You need to add up all the answers to the security questions and follow the trail from the door with that number on it. Good luck!

1 SHORT CIRCUIT ☐ LETTER
+
2 BREAK IN ☐
+
3 NUMBER CRUNCHIN' ☐ ☐
=

DOOR NUMBER: ☐

1 2 3 4 5 6 7 8 9 10

Arrgh! That dirty mongrel set up a booby trap behind the door! By the time I cut myself free of this mess, he's going to be long gone! Thanks for nothing, kid!

Alright! We've got him! Thanks to you Sabretooth is gonna be behind bars for a long, long time! Way to go, bub, with my claws and your brains, we make a pretty good team!

CONTINUED FROM PAGE 41

GAMBIT, MY FEELING IS THAT YOU SHOULD JOIN THE OTHER X-MEN QUICKLY! THERE'S NO TELLING WHAT *ELSE* APOCALYPSE MAY HAVE IN STORE. XAVIER OVER.

GOT *DAT* RIGHT, MON AMI. ME AN' JEAN HEADIN' UP NOW. GAMBIT OUT.

AT THAT MOMENT, HIGH ABOVE THE EAST COAST, THE *SHIELD** HELI-CARRIER MOVES ABOVE THE CLOUDS AS DIRECTOR NICHOLAS FURY MEETS WITH PENTAGON OFFICIALS...

* STRATEGIC HAZARD INTERVENTION EXECUTIVE LOGISTICS DIRECTORATE. -- OO - DARREN

AWRIGHT, GENTS, HERE'S THE SCOOP. COUPLE O' NUKES ARE ON THEIR WAY TO THE U.S FROM MOTHER RUSSIA.

THEY'RE OVER EUROPEAN AIRSPACE RIGHT NOW . I GOT SOURCES IN THE KREMLIN THAT VOUCH FER YELTSIN AN' HIS GOVERNMENT. THEY HAD NOTHIN' TO DO WITH THE LAUNCH.

AND MY SOURCES IN THE RUSSIAN MILITARY SAY DITTO. NOBODY IN THE ARMED FORCE TOOK IT ON THEMSELVES TO TOSS SOME BOMBS AT UNCLE SAM.

14173 02748

5072

I KNOW WHAT YER THINKIN'. WE CAN'T *WAIT* FER THE BIRDIES TO LAND, WE GOTTA RETALIATE *NOW!*

WELL, I'M EXPECTIN' A CALL FROM THE *ONE* GUY ON THE PLANET WHO'S GOT INFO *I* AIN'T GOT.

I'M RECOMMENDIN' WE *DON'T* MAKE A MOVE UNTIL CHARLES XAVIER MAKES CONTACT.

WE AIN'T GOT MUCH TIME... BUT I'M ONLY ASKING FOR A FEW *MINUTES.*

CONTINUED ON PAGE 57

51

JUGGERNAUT

Real Name: **Cain Marko**
Height: **6'10"**
Weight: **900 lbs**
Eye Colour: **Blue**
Hair Colour: **Red**

MUTANT POWERS:

Once the Juggernaut starts moving in any direction he is virtually unstoppable. He possesses apparently unlimited strength and has been known to lift over 100 tons.

CASE HISTORY:

The unstoppable entity known as the Juggernaut is actually Charles Xavier's stepbrother, Cain Marko. Although he is not a mutant, Cain gained his power from an ancient crystal known as the Ruby of Cyttorak that he and Charles discovered during their time as soldiers in Korea.

Although it is seemingly impossible to stop him physically, the Juggernaut's psyche is his one major weakness. Because of this he wears a specially-constructed helmet, which shields his mind.

⊗ SPEED	1
⊗ STRENGTH	1C
⊗ INTELLIGENCE	3
⊗ FIGHTING SKILLS	5

APOCALYPSE

Real Name: **En Sabah Nur**
Height: **Unknown**
Weight: **Unknown**
Eye Colour: **Red**
Hair Colour: **None**

MUTANT POWERS:

Apocalypse has the ability to alter his physical form at will. He can change his size, appearance and even morph parts of his body into weapons.

CASE HISTORY:

The being known as Apocalypse was born over five thousand years ago in Egypt. Due to his strange appearance he was abandoned by his tribesmen as a baby and was found and raised by a raider named Baal.
Once Apocalypse reached adulthood he returned to Egypt and overthrew the Pharaoh Rama-Tut.

For millennia Apocalypse has roamed the planet, manipulating civilisations into war and ensuring that only the most powerful races survive.

⊗ SPEED	8
⊗ STRENGTH	8
⊗ INTELLIGENCE	8
⊗ FIGHTING SKILLS	10

DATA FILES

MAGNETO

Real Name: **Erik Lehnsherr**
Height: **6'2"**
Weight: **190 lbs**
Eye Colour: **Bluish-grey**
Hair Colour: **Silver**

MUTANT POWERS:

As his name suggests, Magneto has the power to manipulate the earth's magnetic fields. Using this, he can manipulate any object that contains iron. He can even use his abilities to affect human beings by controlling the iron in their blood.

CASE HISTORY:

All his life, Magneto has been a victim of bigotry. He was born into a German gypsy family in 1928, but was imprisoned in a Nazi concentration camp during the Second World War.

The young Erik Lehnsherr managed to escape from the camp but could not save his family. After the war, Erik journeyed to Israel where he became friends with Charles Xavier. This friendship did not last due to their radically different views on mutants. Embittered by his past experiences, Erik believed that mutants could only survive if they ruled the planet.

After many years assembling a group of like-minded mutants, Erik renamed himself Magneto and began a terrorist war against humanity.

SPEED	2
STRENGTH	7
INTELLIGENCE	7
FIGHTING SKILLS	8

ENEMIES OF THE X-MEN

The X-Men need YOU!

Welcome, my young friends. As you are well aware I am Professor Charles Xavier, leader of the X-Men. To be an X-Man is no easy job. It is not enough to be a great warrior, you also need to be willing to help mutant-human relations whenever possible.

Take the test I have prepared and discover whether you have the potential to become a member of the X-Men...

TOP SECRET ✖ TOP SECRET

1 WHILST WALKING DOWN THE STREET YOU DISCOVER A YOUNG MUTANT BEING PURSUED BY AN ANGRY MOB. DO YOU...

A) Explain to the crowd that mutants are not a threat and try to soothe their fears, whilst attempting to not use your powers unless someone's life is in danger.

B) Keep on walking and don't get involved. It's not your fault these guys have got a problem with mutants!

C) Use your powers to smite the petty-minded humans and teach them once and for all not to pick on members of the Homo Superior race!

2 WHICH OF THESE ABILITIES WOULD YOU RATHER HAVE?

A) Healing powers, allowing you to rescue and regenerate your fallen comrades in battle!

B) Invisibility, so no one can find you when it's your turn to do the cleaning!

C) Fire generation, allowing you to burn down the human's cities, safe in the knowledge that a glorious new mutant civilisation will rise from the ashes!

3 IF YOU WERE ACCEPTED INTO THE X-MEN, WHICH OF THESE UNIFORMS WOULD YOU PREFER?

4 YOU DISCOVER YOU HAVE THE MUTANT POWER TO FIRE PLASMA BEAMS FROM YOUR HANDS. WHICH OF THESE WOULD YOU RATHER HAVE AS YOUR X-MEN CODENAME?

A) Fire-Flash!

B) Morris the Mutant!!

C) The Destructor! A solid name that will strike fear into the hearts of my oppenents!

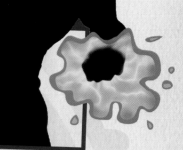

5 CEREBRO HAS PICKED UP A SIGNAL FROM A YOUNG MUTANT GIRL WHO IS IN TROUBLE AND YOU NEED TO FIND HER QUICKLY. WHICH OTHER X-MEN TEAM MATE WILL YOU TAKE WITH YOU?

A) Jean-Grey. Her telepathic powers will be useful to find the girl and help calm her down.

B) Um.... Wolverine? He's good at talking to people isn't he?

C) Pah! I wouldn't need another team mate. I am quite capable of bringing in one little girl by myself!

6 WHICH OF THESE MUTANTS IS NOT AN ENEMY OF THE X-MEN?

A) STORM

B) SCARLET WITCH

C) SABRETOOTH

HOW DID YOU DO?

Mostly A's:
Exceptional! You seem to have just the right temperament to join the X-Men. I am positive that you and your powers will be of great value to my team. You do have mutant powers, don't you?

Mostly B's:
I'm afraid you're not quite what we're looking for. I suggest you brush up on your mutant knowledge before you consider re-applying.

Mostly C's:
Hmmmm.... These results are very disturbing indeed, there's no way I can offer you a place at my academy. It appears you have more in common with Magneto and his brotherhood of mutants than you do with the X-Men. Mark my words, we will be keeping a very close eye on you in the future...

COLOUR X-TREME!

Grab your pens and add some colour to this picture so the X-Men can defeat Apocalypse in style!

56

CONTINUED FROM PAGE 57